Memories

In An Iowa Glass

By: Deon Harris

ISBN- 9798540981804

We Help You SelfPublish Your Book
Crystell Publications
PO BOX 8044 / Edmond – OK 73083
www.crystellpublications.com
(405) 4143991

Printed in the USA

Acknowledgements

This story is dedicated to anyone that has lost someone. For me, it is in loving memory of my dear brother, Myrail "Rail" Harris and my nephew Robert "Rob Raw" Norris. They did not get a chance to see their dreams come true from the manifestation of their total potential. The world is less because of their absence, but hopefully, in the time that they did spend among us, the footprints they left, as memorialized in the words that follow, will serve to instill hope and inspiration into others.

Prologue

One of the best things of the human mind is its ability to capture experiences and gently save them as memories that we can play over and over again.

The two men's lives that are portrayed in the words that follow go to show that is doesn't matter if you actually knew a person to be moved by their story. While we shared the same bloodline, our bond was beyond that, for we were not only related in brotherhood and relation by birth, but we also chose to be as men.

Eventually, we all lose someone that we cherished and long to see again. How they treated us, or how they affected us in the things they did, even simply how they may have said our name. No one called me "lil' bro" like my brother "Rail. We aspire to be better because of these people and in their memory we strive to be more because we know they are watching us. In life we don't want to embarrass them and in their deaths we do not want to disappoint them. We strive for continual affirmation that they are proud of us. That was my brother Rail.

Sinatra made a song, "Did it My Way", that would prove to be my nephew Robert's personal anthem. I have been blessed to have many wonderful nephews and relatives, but we all have that one that holds a special place in our hearts.

Robert would call me "Unc" with such a dedication and smile that it would pierce my heart. I cherish all of my nephews, but Robert looked up to me in such admiration that I found a bond of camaraderie accompanied by a willingness to be better because of each other.

I loved these men with my whole heart, and wherever they are, I hope they see me striving to be a better person, just as I trust that in reading the following pages may bring inspiration to be more by the end of the story than one was at the beginning.

Deon Harris

Memories In An Iowa Glass

CHAPTER 1

Myrail

At birth I was one of three. Apparently I pushed Latiesha out and my other sister followed. Despite what the stories about me portray, I do not remember much before I was six the year I moved in with my mother. Oh, I forgot to mention, my sister and I, we actually have different fathers. My oldest sister passed away before we were one, leaving us to fend for ourselves against our older brothers, the closest in age to us was Myrail, otherwise known as

"Rail".

Growing up in the "Henry Horner" projects of Chicago, Illinois had its novelty, but having "Rail" as a brother was an experience in and of itself. He was the epitome of mischievous, with great cleverness and sometimes even played the bully. When I moved in with him and my even older brother Myron, it was like I was the new kid on the block. "Rail" treated me almost with indifference when he wasn't being flat out mean. Later I would come to realize that early on he was afraid of not being Myron's favorite.

If ever a dare there was, "Rail" was sure to accept the challenge. At times it seemed like utter bravery and at others utter foolishness. He possessed an element of craziness almost approaching insanity for his intensity was often misinterpreted. He was one of those unique people on the planet he had little fear of many things that one should be afraid of.

"Rail" had a reputation for certain things, kind of like a trademark, one of which was pulling every fire alarm in any school he ever entered. It was as if it was a calling for him, a type of galactic obligation of which was bestowed upon him and he would not let the universe down. He would "test the effectiveness of the public school's fire system", he would often admit.

My mother would tell stories of him with a fondness bordering on a reverence almost, about how he would do things. Not for attention, but more driven by an old soul. Like the times he would literally steal food off of people's plates when we had a big meal at grandma's house, and go hide under the front porch and eat it or keep it tucked away in a hidden bag as if he would leave us at any time.

Even though he pushed the patience of many he encountered, he also captured their hearts inevitably winning them over without intent or motive. Everyone that knew him, loved him. He demonstrated character when tested and shared a passion for living that was absolutely contagious.

We had a reciprocal admiration for one another and I knew that he would always have my back just as I had his. Growing up in the projects of any community presented its challenges, ours was no different. Finding solace or a piece of comfort was difficult, but when "Rail" was around you always felt a sense of safety, a luxury that I took for granted only to learn later in life something to be cherished. He was my brother by blood and my best friend by choice.

CHAPTER 2

Robert

My twin sister Latiesha has not always done things right, but one thing she did do right was bring into this world my nephew Robert. I will never forget the day he was born, because I was too. Born in the sense that while I was running the streets ripping things up, I was now an Uncle and that gave me a new found perspective I felt more mature and more responsible. I self implemented a type of honor in me and an accompanying entitlement. This compelled me to run harder and play even harder. I was destined to rule the streets then life got in the way.

In 1999, I got in my car, drove to Chicago and tore Robert out of his environment. To say he was in an environment that was conducive to proper growth would be an understatement and an insult to even the simplest of intellects. He was living in a hell, and at the age of six, I could relate. Even though I couldn't remember much before six, other than living with my aunt, I could feel demons in me that I was certain were there since my birth.

My motivation for going to get him stemmed from a recognition of familiarity he reminded me of...me. Up to that moment I had not spent the time with Robert that I swore I would the day he was born. I was his "Unc" and I really didn't even know him and he didn't know me. That would change, I avowed.

When you are poor, grand gestures are even amplified as such gestures are invaluable and go to the judging of one's character. "If you don't have money, but you have loved ones, you'll be okay. But, having money with nothing else, that is a lonely place. I spent quality time with Robert after that, I even bought him his first bike and taught him how to ride it. I could see the panic on his face and in his breathing, but in his eyes he had a confidence because his "Unc" was with him. He was hit by a drunk driver riding that bike not very long after. How he survived the crash, no one knew, not even the doctors.

Robert had an inquisitive mind, always questioning things and searching for answers to the things he did not know or understand. He had an intellectual capacity that was not challenged enough by his environment, so he forced himself to find other means to pacify his curious nature one filled with an eagerness to be more every day. His surroundings filled him with things that no boy of his age should experience, the kinds of things that shape a character and stay with you forever, no matter how hard you try to move past them. Unable to ease the dramatic events of his adolescent years would prove to influence him greatly, even more than me.

("In 2001 I went to...") prison for sixteen years and that absence from him not only filled me with guilt and remorse, but would serve to be an emptiness that Robert tried to fill even after his mom came down eventually to live with him. In contemplation as I sat in a five by seven cell, I realized that I was imprisoned even before 2001, I was captive to my addiction for my heroin.

I recall a skit from the "Big Tymers" album "I got that work" from "Big Chief". There is a part that goes:

"You coming around scratching ..." and want to blame it on the detergent, no its the dope"

Robert would look straight at me with a sense of seriousness, almost a pleading, and say, "Unc, they talkin' about you".

He was intelligent and intuitive. He was a breath of fresh air in a climate that was always so stale I could breath easier with him around and while I thought I was teaching him he was teaching me. He inspired me as he lifted me up when I thought I was watching over him. I learned about myself and about the life that is to be cherished he was my nephew, he was my blood, he was a gem in the rubble of life he was "Robert".

"Despite all I did ..." and all he had, Robert has a restless spirit. I often thought it was because Cedar Rapids moved so much slower than Chicago, but soon realized that after his mother finally arrived to Cedar Rapids, it was her absence.

Deon Harris

Hey Uncle, How's it been I'm doing good tryin to make it through High School, you know how it is. But, I'm growing up and getting older, and we miss you and love I'm bouta to go to this prom thing with my girlfriend next weekend something I'm look fin forward to ▓▓ and tryin to stay out of trouble... Me I be at home liften weights too tryin to get big like you. But I'll write you some more when get a chance.

CHAPTER 3

Part II: Just like you
Myrail

Poverty does not discriminate. When you grow up in an environment that is conducive for guns, drugs and violence, you become a product of them and that way of life is not uncommon. My older brother Myrail and I however had a choice. While we were a statistic, we didn't have to be, we chose to be. Monetarily we were poor by any definition, but we were rich in a family and parents that loved us and provided for us. They were good examples pops worked hard everyday and mom stayed at home for us. However, moving as frequently as we did left an impression on us and prevented us from engaging in the concept of "rooting" from which to grow in stability and safety. It was a distraction, but it did provide for unique opportunities associated with each new adventure that was the "new neighborhood". We went to about seven grammar schools, each unique in their names as they were in there style: Henry Suder, Nathaniel Dett, Matthew Henson, Perkin Bass, and Guglielmo Marconi, to just name a few. We also lived in many different neighborhoods that took on their own unique identities and named after the junction of two roads, dead presidents or someone that one day did something to affect our area.

No matter where we went, we always found the "hot spots". "It was like a natural attraction ..." that called us, that drew us, an insatiable thirst that was innate in us and we drank until we were full. Our first job was working at Burger King, Myrail worked the flat grill and I mastered the fries, we were a dynamic duo. That place would prove to instill in Myrail a solid work ethic and his love for women, especially Karla Wilbourn, the wife of Tommy Wilbourn that is a situation that appeared destined to be problematic from the start. But, from this relationship spawn my nephew, Myrail Duruis Harris and to his last breath, Myrail was devoted to him and they shared a special filial bond that is unique between a father and a son. The whole situation, as it turns out, worked for everyone Tommy would even go on to officiated Myrail's funeral and the compassion in his voice still rings true in me today. They may have loved the same woman and dealt with the tragedy that comes with such a plight, but they also had respect for one another. Myrail was often a victim of circumstances and timing good or bad.

"I remember a time, for example, when Myrail was off at the "jobs corp "and I was messing around in the kitchen. I ended up spilling scalding grease on my foot and out of nowhere appears Myrail to come to my rescue." He always seemed to know what to do or what to say to makes things better. He told me he loved me without saying the words, but in his thoughtfulness and in his actions. Every year at tax time he would take me shopping with his refund. He would deck me out from top to bottom a ritual that would last into my later years. You always saw him in Rock Revials apparel, and Air Force Ones he dressed to impress and I followed directly in his footprints.

However, our attraction to similar things was not limited to our attire, but other aspects as well especially those things that took so much from so many the freedoms and the lives lost jails and drugs were as frequent and reliable as the sun rising and then setting. Those thing that stayed with us, that keep us connected over the years, still fill me even to this day. I remember the NWA CD "Niggas 4 life" that Myrail picked up as soon as it hit the racks. The beat and lyrics ..." bring me back to him, back to those days we shared together to the times of doing what adolescence do play hard. We would frequent the local district parks"... playing some ball and then head over to the gas stations to offer to fill up the tanks ,or we would go to the grocery store to offer to carry out groceries. We were always trying to make a buck. I remember a time in particular when I helped an elderly lady, who surprisingly..." had a lot of groceries, only to have her, after I had packed all of her bags neatly in her trunk, open her coin purse and take out a quarter and hand it to me so gingerly while staring at me intently with the warning, "now, do not go and spend this all in one place".

Even though we were"... drawn to similar attractions, our personalities and our attitudes..."could not have been more different. He had a temper that blew frequently as he let it out almost immediately when things bothered him. Me, on the other hand, I would push things down, suppress them so I wouldn't have to face them. They would go deep into me allowing me to maintain a much more subtle demeanor. Each of us with our own idiosyncrasies that would prove to influence others, others like my nephew Rob.

CHAPTER 4

Robert

"Robert was not as fortunate as I was..." having Myrail as an adult male figure. Rob was left ultimately to his own devices despite my interest in being a part of his life as mine got in the way. But leaving Rob to fend for himself proved to build his character, but an adversity to authority along the way. As I was fighting my own demons Rob was making his own. Childhood and all it entails and all that it lacks shapes who we become as men. Rob was no exception and as he grew up he developed a sense of arrogance, a type of hubris that served as more of a protective mechanism due to the many insecurities that young men have that grow up without a strong male role model those that are brought up fatherless. But, he always kept it real with me his "Unc".

They say that "absence makes the heart grow

fonder" and when I went to prison in 2001, there was an immediate reactionary phenomenon for when most people turn the other way, Rob turned towards me. More accurately, we turned towards one another, growing closer and closer as we were both in dark places but neither of us admitting it to the other. It was the words unspoken that bound us, a bond that no other thing could break. He kept things positive while I was locked up, but when we were reunited he confided in me the things he and his sister endured during my absence.

The things they had to endure, no children should. When he spoke, he spoke with intent and purpose and demanded your undivided attention, because he didn't mince his words so he expected the same respect in return. Living in "Alda B. Wells" housing complex was like saying like you grew up in hell without any water and there was no salvation. However, he and his sister had a pure heart that kept them going and aided in lifting them up into the hands of a higher power.

Rob was imaginative and creative and I believe that too helped him to persevere. He connected to music as it was a means of self-expression and functioned as an outlet to release the pressures and the stress of the demons "...that resided in him, these things..." that haunted him and tried to steal his happiness. He refused to let the "thieves in the night" take more than he had and that would serve to make him the young man that he was strong and resolute.

CHAPTER 5

Part III: FROM BOYS TO MEN

"It is strange, almost funny..." how time has seemed to have passed so quickly in retrospect but move so slow when you're living it. One day we are wearing each other's clothes, hanging on the streets with our friends and the next we are caring for our own family. Rail would wear Vell's (RIP) "Troops" shoes, and that was a big deal considering how cool the shoes were and that Vell was so much older and well respected in the neighborhood. Vell was the older brother of Lereain Matthews, a good friend of mine even to this day. Those times living on Kenneth, the one between West End and" ... Maypole was never dull, but they paled..." in comparison to the times on Roosevelt and Springfield grandma's house. The lessons learned were endless just as was the fun. The "House of the Harris's" everyday was like a movie with a full cast of colorful characters. The truth be told though, the love and warmth that emanated off of the hollowed walls that held so many memoires was comforting. Being around family like that, one rich in caring and personality would forever be a foundation in my life. It was a house that become a home for so many that have passed; Grandma Sadie B. Harris, Annette Harris, Cleotha Hodges, Johnell Harris, Grgeory Harris, Fernando Hodges, Lula K. Hodges and Rita Steward to name a few of the precious souls that blessed the home with their presence.

In 1984 Michael Jackson, the youngest brother and performer of the group called, "The Jackson Five" was sizzling and the concept of music videos on TV was being introduced to the new era of America it was a smash. I remember spending all of those hours with Rail watching the videos and talking about all of the things that we would do and what we would become as we were moved by the rhythm and lyrics coming off the TV screen. Rail was a rebel in action and I was one at heart. That man that raised us, my father Mr. Charles Boss, instilled morals in us, especially Rail whose biological father, Bobby "Musheen" Frazier, was not as influential until Rail was older. The whole group actually got along, even Pop's Charles and "Musheen". We had strong men around us, mostly on the peripheral, that gave us just enough room to do what kids do, get in trouble.

I remember lighting cigarettes for the adults and taking puffs as I did. "At first, the experience ..." was nauseating but that was soon over weighted" ... by the impression of feeling older and the addictive nature ..." of nicotine that not even young adolescence are immune to. One time Rail used a book of matches and somehow his shirt caught on fire leaving him with second degree burns. He tried to hide it from our mother, but the pain on his face betrayed his attempts. She cared for him with the nurturing hand a mother does and while her voice expressed anger, "...we knew it was from the fear that comes with the concern of one of her babies being hurt, it was not so much about what we had done. "

"One thing we siblings of different fathers did; we stuck together. "It didn't matter who was from who, we all had the same mother and while we were bound by blood we choose to be together a choice that meant more than the blood that flowed through our veins. Those summer days that went by like a flash allowed us to demonstrate the manifestation of the daredevil in all of us. The roller skating that led into grabbing onto the bumpers of cars only to find ourselves challenged by the increasing speed of the cars compared to our skills and the road was not a soft landing place. Yet, we repeated it again and again despite "...the fear of falling. The surge of excitement ..." was more than enough to conquer our fears, and the life that many of us would lead would require courage. We played with reckless abandonment and lived most of our lives the same.

One of Rail's weakness was his poker face, or should I say his lack of one. One time when we were stealing things from the store on the corner of Madison and Laverne"...Rail was so paranoid that the owner could read on his face what we were doing. So, Rail quickly placed everything back on the shelves." When we took off as fast as my third grade legs would carry me, all I could hear was the voice of the store owner yelling, "so, you think you all slick, huh!"

Ditching school in those days was a common event for Rail, so much so that attending school was actually the exception. When we were living on Monroe and Kilbourn, Rail started hanging out with the tough crowd, with the "gangbangers", if you will, and they would "pop the freight" on a daily basis. On one such occasion they popped the lock on a potato chip truck and because they "...could not carry all of the bulky chips, they stashed all of it in the nearby gangway. As young kids, the mere prospect of free, unlimited potato chips".... was too much to pass up. So, we went for a "hike" in the hood." We sat on the playground of Marconi elementary school and ate until we were sick. Later, two of the guys that stole the chips caught up with us and one of them gave me a pass because Rail was part of the lick, but the other was not so considerate and slapped the guy that was with me into next week. To this day "...I know he still feel that sting a little."

Speaking of Marconi Elementary, "...we played some ball for the school. We mostly because the coach lived on our street, not because of our desire or any god given talent our strengths proved to lay in other extracurricular activities. I think our lack of enthusiasm and other interests disappointed the coach because he was under the fallacy that we would evolve into these awesome ball players and that would be our ticket off the streets and away from the penitentiary.

Our interests were as diverse as our personalities. I recall how every year there was a big theatrical production at school. There was always singing and dancing and myself, Rail and my other brother Myron all had parts. Myron had the part of singing the O'Jays' "The Backstabbers", a song our father played frequently so performing it was second nature.

And as for the dance moves, we invented most of them anyways. "...when I was in the sixth grade I was nominated ..." for the lead role and I practiced and practiced"... only to have my voice decide to change at the same time. So, Rail did it ..."instead and he did an amazing job. We had all of the girls screaming, "Harris Brothers"! and being all dressed up in our suits for the first time gave...us a sense of pride." Being on that stage with my brothers all dressed up like that and with all of the girls screaming our names was such an impressionable experience one that we would chase after for the rest of our lives. Being admired like that, standing with one another, brothertobrother, we felt that nothing would stop us. We were the Harris Brothers and we were destined to conquer the world.

CHAPTER 6

Part IV:Living that high Life

Like JayZ in the song, "Where I'm From", the lyrics guide, "I told the world, if I ever blow, I'll let 'em know, just stating what takes place in the ghetto." By the time 1990'91 rolled around the sixties were making a come back drugs were emerging as a common extracurricular and weed was becoming popular again. The "high life" had begun and not a day went by that didn't include "forty Ouncers" and a big bag of weed. The roots were established in the basement of Marlon "Slick" Smith (RIP) loud music, beer and reefer. Without a care in the world we spent day after day doing...well...nothing. With our mother fighting her own addiction".... she expected very little of us and that is what we gave and to the world; very little of anything about anything." Hell, we often thought that we were cool by doing nothing all day. Whatever money we didn't spend on clothes we spent on filling our topps and mugs the weed and beer were flowing. These habits evolved, like most things do. Rail took the lead on the journey that many do not return from, he met dope. Ironically enough, or maybe not so much, his first sixteenth was done up by our mother. She showed us how to cook it, and we knew we had a captive audience, everyone at grandma's place. They would become our best and longest customers.

The place at Pine and Lake was where we met two of "...our lifelong friends, those that became more than brothers in blood; William "Will" Holloway (RIP) otherwise known as "Mackey" and Duane "Duball" Franklin (RIP). I know they are together and in a better place looking in on me and will live in our memories and in the words I write and the stories those that knew them tell. The relationships themselves really didn't foster until they went to Westinghouse High School . Will was a quiet kid that was just going and coming but always looked" fly". His quietness was overshadowed by his style and his way "he was fresh to the death". Ball on the other hand, he was a little younger and more obnoxious and was actually the friend of another guy we knew whose mothers also knew each other. "I am, and always will be, reminded of how ..."small the world is sometimes. That friend was Ben and his mother was Areatha Ann Roberts (RIP).

"By the time our house had become the"hot spot" and we were in the streets most of the time and working legitimate jobs the other hours left in the day." School was attended if there was ever enough time and seldom was there. Dre's album "the Chronic" depicted the era with lyrics, "like we always do about this time" and Geto Boys, "till death do us part", kickin it through the fifteen inch woofers on the back porch, gettin' high and drunk off beer and life it was a time to embrace. We would play ball in the large porch area always showing off, especially Myrail when the girls were around. It had been years since we were on that stage at Marconi Elementary but the brothers were just "showin' out" differently. The competition between us for the affection of the opposite sex was bound to arise and it did. Rail took to it directly, even letting everyone know if you were wearing his clothes what was once something brothers did that showed a bond, Rail now turned into a demonstration of entitlement and superiority.

In those days there was a family called the Gladneys and I was associated with them as both of my brothers had "associated" with two of their daughters, "...with one resulting in another of my nephews; Daveon Gladney." Day after day of living like this eventually became so common that we didn't recognize the error of such ways. Taking little responsibility "...when playing like an adult would prove to have its consequences." It would not be until later that we would feel the ramifications of such choices.

Those days would prove to influence us more than any others as we were at those ages"... of being impressionable and with abilities..."and those experiences shaped us mentally and behaviorally. Our habits became a normality "...we were hustlers and those moments our innocence was lost..."or should I say given away by our own choices. The positivity we could offer was replaced by a numbness to aspiration and a proclivity to take the path less restricted fast money outweighs a good days work for a decent wage. We lived in a world of illusions, thinking that life was meant to be as it was easy and rich with all those things we desired. Selling drugs was easy, it was the not getting caught part that demanded ones attention or focus. You didn't only have the authorities, but the "stick up man" and anyone else "...trying to steal all that you had "money and drugs everyone around you wanted a piece and wanted it at our expense.

Inevitably Rail and I graduated to heroin. We tried it together for the first time searching for that "silver lining in the sky "only to be left holding the silver foil with a little residue on it. A residue that was more powerful than my own mind. It was as if we knew that we were leading our lives in the wrong direction, talent so wasted. But, instead of changing direction, we just went further into the great divide of a black hole of drugs and money. We were doing different things "...expecting a different result, and we certainly...",did get different results by going harder on heroin. The results were not of the positive kind even though the demon made you think everything was all right all those years of being misunderstood and misjudged now vanished in the puff of smoke. It was like sand on a mirror being blown off by a warm summer breeze.

CHAPTER 7

Demons and Fates

.....We started as "shakers" and "baggers": that led to getting some stuff of our own from the neighborhood "drug king pin" at the time, a true street legend Chi /KTown/"64 Puff". "He just happened to be Uncle of a very close friend of ours; he was "Yattie" Puff's blood nephew. So, we would be shakin' and baggin' the stuff at another guys house, a guy as old as our dad, but he loved the dope. His name was Rod (R.I.P) and he was dropping some real gems on us, the consummate story teller, and all kind of bull jive just to try and get some of our stuff. So, we made a deal with him he could get some product as long as we could use his place in the cut. After all, the last thing we wanted was to be raided in our homes. As the demon had him under its control the deal was an easy one to make for him he granted us access to his apartment and to use it as our laboratory.

As fate would have it, one day of shaking and bagging we decide to try some off the corner of a playing card uncut stuff that is. That was the day that I met my main demon that would haunt me for the rest of my life. That's the thing about them, "...once they are in, it is almost impossible ..."to get them to leave. My life would never be the same. We kept ridin' that wave or sailing that ship whichever euphemism you want to use we were in a foreign state "...that made everything perfect. It was the closest thing to nirvana or so we thought. We became a slave to the product so much that we kept coming up short with the supplier. So, we had to go to the "store" the big suppliers, to get our product. We even came up short with them, but they were making so much money that they didn't seem to mind as much as "64 Puff'. However, we did have an advocate in our cousin, Richard "Richie Rich", he always had our backs. So, the "store" man went easy on us even when we came up short typically a very serious matter.

Later, Rail would tell me about the day one of the older ladies in our building , one that had stopped using years ago, saw what was going on and once said to him, "Ya'll boys are gettin' in the big leagues now". Only if we knew what that would come to mean for us in the future. Its funny how you think you are fooling people, when all the while they see your game and the only one you are fooling is yourself.

Less than a year from then, Rail caught his first small case going "big time", brought "big attention", and that equated to "big heat". "Accordingly, by year three, he had caught a "big case". We were so messed up in those days that we even misplaced ..."some guns that "Richie Rich" had given us for protection, bullets and all. I understand that even "Richie Rich" is in jail today and mourns the events of Rob and Rail.

The big case with Rail had to do with an alleged armed robbery the irony was, we were making money so what was the point. There was apparently a big raid and the small time guys, those dealing with petty disorderly conduct issues, claimed to have seen him arrested and the gun too. This was in 1993 and I would not see Rail again until late 1996. Is a few minutes of "indiscretion worth years of absence?" I often contemplate the decisions we made over those years those moments when consequences appear not real only to find out they are very real. I was so far down the rabbit hole, I barely talked with Rail. "Oh, we spoke a few times here and there, and every once in awhile we might share a picture or two." Knowing he was there tore at me and I knew I didn't want to be living the life I was living, but I never fully committed to stopping and the demons can hold on as long as you let them and I let them.

On a random day, one with no particular significance, I began to design an armed robbery "...with the guy I mentioned earlier; Ben. It was going to be an "inside" job, an "Ocean's12" kind of thing." I sat and conjured up this plan to rob a restaurant where I knew a guy who worked there. I remember sending Rail a money order and a letter riddled with information about what I was going to do and told him that if it all went well I would be sending him more money. I added, that if it didn't go well that he would need to save me a bunk at the "terridome". Well, my partner in the endeavor got arrested, but he didn't implicate me so I got off. "What did I do next?" I bough some dope and ..."sent Rail another money order. The only lesson I learned is" ... how important is it not to tell on another. Never mind the..."illegalities for if you are not caught that makes the indiscretion less...of an indiscretion.

I can only imagine how tough it was for Rail in prison at such a young age of nineteen. Understand that I was even younger than him when we were shakin' and baggin' and trying to run the streets. Cook county jail in and of itself was a school of graduation, in that if you made it out alive, and in one piece, you had obtained manhood. You either fought your way through your sentence or knew people to protect you, Rail did both. While he was gone, things changed Duball and Will passed away and I dove deeper into my habit, getting tighter and tighter with the demons that were taking my soul. Prison takes more than your freedom and liberty, it takes those experiences and memories that you will never have a chance to make again.

In 1996, right before Rail was to come home, I was awarded a $62,000 settlement. I sent $2,500 to Rail and then proceeded to blow threw the rest. I received it in June, and by December when I went to pick Rail up from the Greyhound bus depot, I was asking him for twenty bucks. To which he rightfully replied, "you blew through all that cash and now you want some from me just when I get out? Hell no!". "At first I was deeply hurt, but I was ..."so happy to have him home that I realized quickly that he was right. I had blown a great opportunity to use that money to make a difference to get out and stay out. Instead, I kept hustling and that led me to dropping off a box of something in someone's car that had left a fresh $100 dollar bill "...on the front seat." It was the "gorilla in me" I would always rationalize I seldom took responsibility for my actions it was always the gorilla. The demons in me "...had existed for longer than I; they were stronger..."and they would always win"... as long as I let them stay and continue to feed them what they lived off ofmy soul."

Rail quickly acclimated to the life of freedom and found himself right back into the similar pattern he was in before his incarceration. Hanging out with the same people in the same environment is destined to form the same man, unless he decides he wants to change that is. Rail and I had been exposed to a certain life style and certain expectations for so long it had become our benchmark, it became our embedded archetype so we endeavored to make it happen. Rail would go on to connect with his high school sweetheart, and I use the descriptive "high school" not because he met her at high school, because he rarely went, but because they were at the age one SHOULD be attending high school.

By the summer of 1997 I had been sent to boot camp and Rail had moved to the south side of town and our interactions became less and less. By November I had made it to the halfway house on the west side and visited with Rail a few times, but we were drifting apart while I was drifting "...even closer to my demons. If that were ..."even possible .I decided to relocate to Cedar Rapids Iowa and leave everyone behind. I was destined to pave my new path." I hooked up ..." with my cousin "Munchie" (RIP) and his pops Terry Brooks (RIP) and headed west to stake my claim.

I should have known how this chapter of my life would end considering how it started. We no more than stepped a foot into Iowa and Terry was raided by the Feds. But, with a record of poor decisions, I thought I would make a different decision I would stay in Iowa. I would visit Rail when I went back home and we would have a great time and he was always positive and talking me up about how successful I had become. He was my big brother and despite all that had happened between us I desired his affirmation and love. "I found him a place..." compliments of my then girlfriend, Tiffany Hegarty (RIP) and I was able to supply his clients with product too.

He settled into a one bedroom apartment and things went well at first, but with two strong personalities, conflict was sure to arise. It did. When my Pops, Charles Boss, was visiting things came to a head, and the explosion between Rail and myself could have destroyed a foundation of our friendship that took a lifetime to build had it not been for the presence of my father. He intervened and shared some words that made us think as we parted ways. Today, I am not even sure what the argument was about, and who won, but every time you would ask Rail he would always say that, "he won". To me it never really mattered who won, because there was no winner when drugs and egos collided. The aftermath and fallout "...can be catastrophic, but the love deep within us that was planted and rooted ..." in us by and through our shared hardships, allowed us to overcome this misunderstanding.

Rail and Aletha got their own place and there was enough money being made for everyone; "the mo the merrier"! However, no one realized that we were still living the kind of lives that end up on the front page of the paper or in the back section along with the time of the wake. We were making similar decisions, only the stakes were higher and the numbers had a lot more zeros behind them. The money was coming in and it was coming in fast and we were all holding on for the ride. The brothers were making it rain.

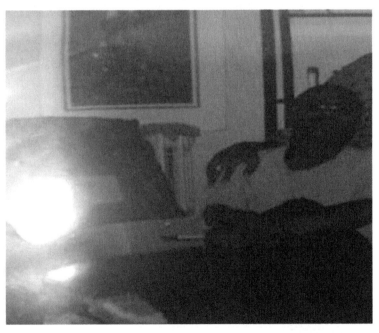

CHAPTER 8

Robert

"One thing I am proud of is that I never did get high ..." with Robert. It seems like I got high with every one of my relatives but him. For some reason it is as if that made our relationship more pure as it was not tainted and the devil wasn't in between us holding us together by a bond of addiction. He never saw me under the influence in the present. For people who are high, they think they feel awesome, but they look like hell sagging postures, squinting eyes and barely able to hold their head up at times. A deplorable depiction of self worth and control. Thankfully, Robert did not see me in such a state of disorientation.

The irony is that whenever I would see him smoke or drink I would remind him that, "real players don't mess with anything that's going to mess up gods temple" and all he would do was laugh that infectious laugh. However, despite what he knew about me, he would always show me respect and respond, "Unc, I am going to stop". The biggest part was the company he kept, because he wasn't weak or easy to influence. It was simply as the saying goes, "you become like the company you keep". I only wish I had been a better role model and that he could have kept my company and had been the better for it and he to his younger sister Lydia Harris.

CHAPTER 9

Part V:Uncaged Minds
Myrail

My lineage is replete with two long standing conditions: drug addiction and incarceration. I don't know if you can call the consequences of one's choices a curse, but to have such a demonstrated proclivity, from generation to generation, to fall victim to the power of the demons and the loss of freedom, borders on the supernatural or mystical. "Socioeconomic statistics suggest certain..." probabilities of outcomes and accordingly, Myrail's first stint would not be his last. He would get his" ... "...second offense ,it was not as long as mine. Nonetheless, it was a lengthy seventeen year sentence at the time did not fit the crime."

"You do time or it does you. The condition ..." of being separated from those people you love and the loss of those freedoms and liberties which you appreciate is coupled with being placed with people that you would otherwise most likely not associate with its who they take you from and who they put you with. I love my family and I am very proud of many of them "...for what they have endured. They have fought many battles and when all the odds were against them, they prevailed. It is a testament to their ..." intestinal fortitude. But how many relatives have to go through hardship, how many have to fall victim to the demon, how many need to suffer the conditions of incarceration before we learn the lesson? At what point does one decide they need to change?

Rail was subject to a federal indictment in 2005, one that resulted in a seventeen year sentence. Granted, he was familiar with the system of things due to his first bit but facing such a lengthy sentence will test any man's mettle. I followed Myrail's first stint with one of my own, but mine ended up as a thirty piece 360 month sentence. I do not know if it's "one-up" your brother kind of thing but seventeen or thirty, each is its own devastating reality.

Inevitably, something happens that causes a life to change when you live like we were living if the demons don't kill you, then a bullet or prison will. When the Feds got me in 2001," ...I told Myrail that I was done and that he needed to go "back to Chicago. Instead of heading my advice he just replied," Lil' bro Scotchie Moe, you were just doin' it wrong". This attitude would lead to his fresh seventeen. There are some lessons that can be learned in more than one way, but for me it always seemed to be the hard way. "When I heard about Myrail's sentence I sat and envisioned us ..." celling together, "...for it was not unheard of "at all" for brothers to..." serve time together. Then, it hit me I was in prison to serve a thirty year sentence and my big brother was looking at his own seventeen and I had a hint of pride in the prospect that he and I might serve it together. I knew at that moment at the meeting of a dark history and an uncertain future, that things needed to change, that I needed to change. "As fate would have it..." they sent Myrail to Terra Haute and not to Pekin FCI where I was housed. "They left me alone looking in the mirror ..." that reflected back a stranger. "It would be a stranger that I would need to come to terms with if I was ever change." Something was stirring inside of me, I could not explain it, I just felt it. With Myrail going to Terre Haute that meant I would need to find my own path, my own journey, one that would have me walking with a different heart.

We corresponded the best we could within the limitations set forth by the BOP as it pertains to

"...incarcerated family members communicating "with one another. We knew a lot of the same people and would send pictures to one another through an outside party, one of them being Maruwa "TRoll" Thomas who kept us with flow of pictures. Eventually, most of the contact stopped "...but from time to time someone new would come to Pekin form Terre Haute that knew Myrail..." and when they found out who I was they would always mention how Myrail talked about his "Lil' brother Scotchie Moe". Well, that's me, a man trying to find his was through the shadow of a big brother. "Time, and how a man spends it, determines how he matures," how he changes. Myrail told me about a time when he showed another inmate a picture and the inmate recognized a girl in the picture but not me. Then Myrail instructed him to look a little closer. The man could not believe that it was me in the picture for he had known me twenty-five years ago. After all of the years, "...this man recognized a part of me, but there I sat not knowing any part of myself." I still didn't know who I was or what I was meant to be.

Myrail stayed affiliated with his associations from the street, but when word came out that drug offenses that did not have gang affiliations may receive time cut in their sentences, he gave up any such associations. My brother wanted to go home. At Pekin I met two guys from Terre Haute that would"... go on to become great friends; "Trouble" Martell Lee and "Mack Strong" Joseph Riely. Martell is doing exceptionally well out in society, whereas, "Mack Strong" is back in prison." I enjoyed both men's company and will always remember ...our time together and our friendship.

"With Rail in Terre Haute an myself in Pekin, serving a combined..." forty-seven years, the legacy of the Harris brothers had been thrown into a different".... direction than we had promised each other so many years ago watching MTV inspired by the lyrics. "had inspired us. Those memories floated through my head as do many of those lyrics like a title on a page I was just not sure how I fit into the grand scheme of things. I was often told by others of the potential I had but as I sat in a Federal Correctional facility staring at a brick wall and thirty years I questioned that assessment. While my older brother, a man I looked up to, sat and faced a seventeen year sentence, something wasn't right and I could feel it in my core. The world that we were destined to rule had turned its back on us and in that realization was a loneliness words cannot describe.

CHAPTER 10

Robert

"Robert was subject to the Harris..." Family curse, something that the harder you tried to escape from the stronger it would hold on to you. Robert was charged with attempted Murder in Linn county. "The charged were dismissed..." but the message held to Robert he was making the wrong decisions. This incident would prove to influence Robert enough to keep him out of trouble the remainder of his life. Robert was a good kid at heart, but his upbringing lacked certain aspects that led him to try and find answers in the street. The problem was, he was never taught what questions to ask. "They saying goes, "you only do what you know". Well, Robert knew enough to know that he needed answers and the problem was he didn't know where else to go but the streets. He was no pushover and his training in the boxing ring when he was younger showed through as he got older and bigger. Behaviorally however, Robert was very impressionable and as a result he was very susceptible to being a product of his environment, whatever that environment was. From my perspective, he was let down by all of those around him, including me. He needed an environment conducive for positive change to be a better man, not to be a better hustler.

Robert had the heart of a lion, a personal characteristic that he inherited from the family gene pool. In particular, an aunt Susan "SueSue" and a cousin named Willie "Will Will" Harris"... each of them spoken of in great regards as to their temperament..." and getting things done when needed. Myrail would even reach out to Robert at times when a situation arose that required his special talent.

Robert was a clay that we molded a little here and a little there. Never was it our intent to harm him or make him into something he was not meant to be. But as the potters, we were so inundated with our own lives that it was an unrealistic expectation. We have a responsibility to those that follow and in such authority we can fall short and forget that what we do matters it matters in the today and for the tomorrows. This is something death and destruction have taught me"... a lesson that I have learned that will never be..."forgotten.

CHAPTER 11

Part VI: My Lil' Man
Robert

"The older I get ,the more I realize..." that which I do not know. While years separated Robert and I, we both learned from one another. While he confided in me, those things most personal to him, I realized how similar and how different, we really were. In such confessions I saw the similar struggles, the similar aspirations, but also the different perspectives. Those differences however gave insight for each of us. Robert was full of life and embraced living not just existing. He reminded me what life was about it wasn't about getting older, it was about staying younger. Age is just a number, but the mindset (mental state) can be the ever sought after "fountain of youth".

During the period of our intercourses, I

witnessed Robert excel at many things. Just as fast as he rose, he would also fall. One day he has a nice job and comfortable place to live and the next he is unemployed with no car or place to live. But he was a fighter. His journey included one of the spirit and his religion, but like all of us, he would get lost along the way.

I vividly remember a time that myself and a partner of mine, RIO, aka "Goldie", were driving to lunch from work. I was fresh out of the joint and whenever we were in the car I would find myself staring out the window entranced by the wondrous life about me. On such occasion Goldie spotted Robert walking down the street. Sure enough, it was him. "Hey Nephew" I hollered as Goldie pulled over to the curb. "Hey Unc! Hey Goldie" Robert replied with a youthful exuberance. The sun shown off his face revealing lines I had not noticed before and he was all dressed up now, he was wearing his Muslim attire including the Kufi. "What's up Nephew?" I asked and he told Goldie and I all about how he was at court fighting for the custody of one of his children. The story brought back memories when he would come by with his son Ashir and the three of us would just hang out. By the time the conversation was over and we pulled away I already missed him I missed the days gone by that were so seemingly insignificant at the time, but meant everything now. That is one thing that prison will do to you.

Robert also functioned in the capacity of my "hair care professional" he was my barber. "Lining me up" and making me ...'look fresh was a serious matter back in those days and he would make the time to take care of me at his place or mine. During those times we would talk about everything I don't know what it is about barbers and bartenders, but they seem to be the best listeners. Robert, being much more than that, made it even easier to share so many personal things with him and he with me.

We often talked about women and how they can mess with a man's mind and the games they play that often include us but are usually directed at other women. A species, we decided, we would never truly understand but we loved them anyways.

You can tell a man's conviction by his manner and tone, so, when it came to his children, Robert was...tenaciously attentive...driven to be their father. He wanted to be present like his father before him was not. While the department of Social Services pretended to be helping, Robert felt they were just in the way of their family dynamics. Birth is a miracle no doubt, but just because the man does not give the birth should not mean he did not have equal rights as the mother a concept that did not seem consistent in his dealing about custody.

Just as Robert was many wonderful things, he also had a dark side. His experiences growing up and his dealing with the devil (drugs) only conjured a greater darkness that could create vast dysfunction. He had a passion for all things, constructive and destructive. It was just his way. He balanced his demons the best he could through prayer and by working on his own personal development, to be more than his upbringing would suggest.

Sitting in the barber shop watching Robert do his thing, seeing his barber's certificate hanging on the wall behind him gave me a great sense of pride. He was always promoting positivity and he would have my books available for sale. I would always tell him that when the Youtube movie came out about my first book "Dog Food", he would play the part of me. He would smile a smile that reciprocated the pride. By the time Robert had built a rather substantial clientele he decided to move back to his own place and save on the cost of a booth fee"... and other people "in his business". He was selective in who he worked with and expanded his services to include tattooing and micro eyeblades. He was talented in those things that mattered to him most the passion he possessed drove him to excel and that same passion led him down many paths. He was the father to many children, and of those I knew of, he fought to have relationships with them despite the noncooperation of the biological mother at times.

He left behind a lineage of beautiful children, each unique in their own way all talented and capable. As commercialized as the advancement of technologies has made certain things and the antisocial aspect associated with many of the applications, YouTube and Face Book have provided a platform where memories may live on. For Robert, we find him in his music and his spirit flows from his Instagram page. I saw a boy grow into a man despite the obstacles placed before him. He battled his demons as we all must do eventually, but he never lost sight of what was most important family. He is my "lil' nephew" and I am his "Unc", now and forevermore.

CHAPTER 12

Part Vll:Brother 4 life
Myrail

I have made choices in my life that have carried consequences resulting in the losses germane to a quality of life: my liberties and freedom. Loss is seldom easy and often difficult, but there is a correlation between the two that can be made: act and consequence. But when a person is taken from you for no apparent reason there is no rationalization and when they are dear to you, like Myron is to me, the impact rips at your very existence. "The sadness buries you in al kinds of emotions..." and the pain is almost unbearable. Oh, how I miss my friend, my brother.

In the absence of Myrail, "...those things that had been taken for granted" between us, become apparent and I am filled with a regret and remorse. For life has no rules when it comes to the time it gives. Over the years we would make it a point to try and talk every day, even when we were incarcerated. Other than my other brother Myron, Myrail was the closest person to me we shared more than a mother at birth, we shared our lives our experiences our tribulations and triumphs.

Just recently I was at a book review and sale event for one of my books and I met a man that knew Myrail. When I introduced myself he recognized my last name and when I told him who my mother was he immediately connected me to Myrail; "your lil' brother who was coming home who wrote the book", he exclaimed. "how did you know that? "I replied in equal excitement. "Your brother told me, I use to work with him."

Moments like those stir in my a bipolarity that is exhausting to know my brother thought so highly of me and knowing that he is gone. Even in his absence he speaks for me, he shows me the pride he has in me my brother looks down on me with favor as I look to him above.

It is no secret that Myrail had a gang affiliation; "Finball" 4 corner hustler. However, his days of "gang banging" were far gone, but from time to time I would over hear him talking to another person about the past or when he would connect to someone on face book reminiscing. I always knew about the associations as we grew older, as every once in a while he would refer to someone as "solid", that was his way of letting me know he was still a brother from the streets.

Watching Myrail was not my first exposure to such a world, for my family on our Mother's side showed us both first. While there were great times, that type of lifestyle brought tragedy as well. Watching my father, one of the coolest men I knew, breakdown over time because of the loss of his two brothers, Melvin and Charlie Boss (RIP) taught me a lesson that no text book can. "My heart compels me to hold onto those..."memories in my mind for they give me purpose and in that purpose a strength from my family past. They reach out to me and remind me to not let them down and to make something of myself.

Myrail was also, at times, a clown. We would hang out almost every Sunday and do laundry or something together and he would get me laughing so hard I thought my stomach would hurt for a week. I would laugh so hard I would cry and in these memories it is hard to stop. The gentleness that was in him allowed him to express humor as he did, just as his pride let him "show off" too. He use to like to take a bunch of money, for example, and spread it all over his dining room table "wanna eat?" would ring in my ears to be hungry for the dollar bills. To see him cuddle with his wife, Mrs. Leta D.

Harris, and see him playing with his grandson, Armani, I saw a calmness and preciousness. There was never a dull moment around him, his enormous personality demanded attention and you either embraced his character or you did not. "He was selective on who he let ..." in, but when you were in, he made you laugh and he made you feel important.

When I look at my other brother Myron I see Myrail so clearly. "When I look at his boys I see him too" Myrail lives on in so many ways, so as we have let him go in the flesh he remains in spirit by revealing himself as he does in my brother and those sons and in the stories that we tell and the songs that we sing. My ears hear his music and my heart feels the glory that is Myrail's as he is in a better place. He brought joy with him and left some with me so I may remember his way, he was my friend, he was my brother, and I was his "lil' Scotchie Moe".

CHAPTER 13

Part VIII: The Memories Never Fade
Rail "The last Ride"

"I'm legit and they can't do nothin' to me" could be the lyrics to a hit song, and they were, to the song of Rail's life. When we would cruise the streets, whenever we saw the police, those words would melodically flow from him. A kind of personal anthem after having served so many years in prison. A day doesn't go by that I don't think of him and at times the memories sneak down my cheeks forever reminding me of the power of love and the thankfulness I have to God for having Myrail in my life. It is strange how, the more we hurt from another passing, the more blessed we feel for having known them, having shared life's experiences with them the pain somehow serving as a reminder of such blessings. The adage, "it is better to have loved and lost than to have never loved at all" whispers in my mind as the burning sensation that still fills my chest when I reminisce of those days with "Rail".

I can see him tapping the steering wheel, bopping to the tunes while always looking sharp even in the dark. The designer shades and fresh threads;

"Aw, its gonna be the Rail show, foreal, sometimes you can catch him on chill mode and he ridin' around listenin' to some soul music, now he's on his Goldie 'The Mack' thang especially puffin' that cigarette"

He was always there for me picking me up from the halfway house in the Dodge "Magnum" or cruisin' the streets in his new Lincoln Continental "when he was driven' that hotrod Lincoln you couldn't tell him nothin', cuz he was hearin' you only thinkin' of him". On a crisp fall day on our way to Taco Bell, Rail played over and over again the JayZ beat from the mix "Dec 4", he was rubbing my head with one hand with the other on the wheel, I felt like a kid all over again. It didn't matter how old we got, I was his lil' Scotchie Moe and he was my big bro "Rail".

I had moved into the same apartment complex as Rail and in August of 2020 we were hit by the Derecho Hurricane that wiped out power for miles. I was hanging out talking with some guys,

"Shakey" and "Boo", in the housing complex and I saw the lights coming off Rail's car so I headed in his direction. You ever see something from a distance and despite the distance you still feel close? I had this experience, a moment frozen in time as I stared at my brother so far away, but yet still so close to me. "There's one gas station still runnin' I guess off of generators," Rail greeted me with. He had his grandson already tucked in back and asked me if I wanted to go with. At first I was hesitant, and then something inside spoke to me, urging me to go with. I was lost in his smile as a gleam flickered in his eyes. It was as if I was transcended an out of body experience almost, but one that I would not become aware of until later as I reflected on that day, on that moment, on that ride for it would be the last one we would share as brothers.

I remember heading out to see his wife at work and he would always give the biggest "Rail show" whenever she was around we never spoke of it, her and I, but it was his way of showing us how much he really cared for us how important we were to him.

Notorious BIG, featuring JayZ, "I love the dough" Project Pat "The Life we live" and Plies, "Ritz Carlton" would frequently beat out of his car. Oh, how he loved that music, how it seemed to fill his soul and raise his spirits. The beat, the rhythm, the words, all in a melody that spoke to him in such a way.

In August of every year we would all get together to celebrate our father's birthday. This year, with all of the electricity out proved to be one of the best, because"... we made the best of what we had...".We gathered at the park and played games and hung out without a care in the world. While most were worrying about no power, we were enjoying the day in one another's company. As the sun was setting and the night started to encroach"... from the peripheral the car lights came on all at once, like a ..."stage hand just "hit the lights" right on cue. They were all on Rail. He was still"... and silent with his bowed." He slowly raised his head with his eyes still closed and from him emanated soft gentle words, his aria for his wife his expression of love. He swayed and even slow danced with our mother to "step in the name of love". The lyrics from RKelly flowed flawlessly from my brother's heart. He embraced the moment in such song and shared it with all of us as he sang the melody into the night that was closing in on us. It was magical, it was a moment out of perfect.

The hardest time for me began in 2001 the year I would start serving my thirty-year sentence. I would not see Rail until 2016 fifteen years of which I experienced some of the darkest times, alone. We had kept in contact over the years via telephone or letters, but to see him in the flesh and to hear his words directly from him were comforting. During some of those years he spent his own time in prison and even then he would send people to see me, even the mother of his children's grandma , Patricia "Poochie" Steele (may she RIP). My heart aches for the loss and goes out to her family as I still breathe each breath more appreciated than the previous one as the frailty of life we are so often reminded of with the passing of the ones we love and cherish.

I was there when Rail did his first face book posting, live from a restaurant on 29 July 2018. I was the one he called when he wanted to get back into working out I was the one...the one...that was his brother and his friend in all things. There was no one like my brother Rail. While Myron looked like him, his personality made him the unique kind that you know God threw away the mold when he was done because he was so very, very pleased.

Chapter 14

Robert "the longest ride"

Inevitably, death comes to us all. It can be as subtle as in the middle of the night "...while you sleep or as subtle..."or as bold as a rush in the middle of broad daylight. When it takes the young or those with so much more life to live it is hard to accept. Losing Robert so young "...is one of the many tragedies of my life and one that cuts ..."deep. I remember the first time he came to visit me in prison, he was no more than fourteen years old, but he was so brave and mature. He expressed to me how much he missed me and how he looked forward to spending more time with me when I was released this was in 2006. With an outdate of around 2028, that was such an innocently bold statement on his part. There was conviction and sincerity in how he said it and how he seemed to look upon me with an admiration. Moments like that motivated me, not only for the man I would become, but more significantly the man that I would not.

We would talk for hours about all kinds of things. He would often express how he hated having to go and ask the neighbors for food eggs, milk or sugar. His pride allowed for an embarrassment that would drive him to do certain things, shaping the man he would become. His natural tendency to protect his mother caused Robert to distrust the ".. men that came around and developed, ultimately, into a ..." distrust of most authority figures. It is strange how we can form a disliking for the things we want most when we do not get them. Robert wanted, Robert needed, a strong male rolemodel in his life. He needed one that would stay anyways. "Robert had neither, and from it he grew strong..." in many ways and not so strong in others.

Robert was filled with an angst that he burned off through boxing"... but never completed rid himself of..." He always stayed in top physical condition an alpha male in a world where there were many that he saw but few that knew him. Despite his shortcomings, as we all have, he was of strong character and would serve the bloodline well.

Every time I hear "Lil' baby feat. Yo Money Bag" "All of a sudden "tears form in my eyes as it brings me back to a time Robert was cutting my hair and the song came on the radio and we danced the whole thing through. I can see his moves and the expression of happiness on his face even today. I introduced him to the likes of "Nipsey Hustle" (RIP), while he introduced me to Lil' Durk and King Von and Pop Smoke (may they RIP).

They say that "the pen is mightier than the sword" and in the inference of the adage, the pen does have power for good just as for harm. The letters I received from Robert while I was incarcerate were like a beacon of light for a ship that had lost its way a communication of means that brought me closer to a safe harbor. In prison you have the opportunity to see many things in a different perspective as the drugs have been flushed from your system and the interference of daily life is not so intrusive. You are often left alone with your thoughts with your memories and all of the emotions that go with them.

Facing a thirty year sentence as a result of some one telling on you has its challenges. Robert shared with me on several occasions, while incarcerated and upon release, the words to "make you hate me", paying homage to his Unc that was informed on. He had such a versatile artistic approach and had recorded so many songs on you tube from his make shift recording studio out of his house. He was a boy with great potential that developed into a young man with many talents. He had respect for himself that was made evident in his demeanor and in his dress, he always looked the part fresh. He drew attention to himself and at times more than he wanted but often less than he deserved.

On a long summer drive, after a speaking engagement in Waterloo, Iowa, Robert and I talked about life, about expectations and dreams and how they often met somewhere in the middle. That summer's day commute would be the longest drive I would ever take with Robert one that I will always remember because it wasn't long enough we had so many more miles to go together.

Deon Harris

Memories In An Iowa Glass

Unc whas up! 08746-029

7-18-15 Im coolin just out in Moline, IL
8: Slepeworking dis welding job. I got paid every
friday. Once I got my place Im send ya
some money. Ima hold on to this job
cuz they pay good and I like it. Plus.
Im tryna be stable to get my two kids
Raniya & Kaiye Im good on court shit
no cares' staying out the way just tryna
make some of myself.
    Iwork Sun-Thur 9:00pm-2:30am
Im just geeked to get back to work.
you know people don't wanna deal with you
if you aint got nothing. But yeah
I don't feel he going into the whole
Story with my mom Im just moving
forward cuz I cant saved everybody.
Ladreya is not my daughter not my problem.

Unc you got some questions for me
I don't have much to say at this
time besides I love you and cant
wait till you got out. Ima stay in
touch just keep the letters comming
Ima stay based be protected sex
cuz des girls want kids out here I
think thats the age for them or something
up with the early 20s. I sent
lil pics Ill send more just
let me know I aint into it with
nobody just coolin and fighting for
custody of my kids. Love you

89| P a g e

Deon Harris

Friday
2:31

Dear Uncle,

Hey, I've been missing you. How Have you been doing? Good I hope. Well if you wanted to know I'm in 7th grade about to be in 8th in a few months. And I'm going to be a teenager too. Everybody is doing good. I'm doing better in School My mom is doing good in school too. But, the DCFS Stuff is getting in our way. My mom is going to write you too. And Send you some pictures. LaDieya is getting so big, with her bad butt. My moma and Doahld are getting along good. And with me too. Sorry it's been so long since I've written you but, things are so busy. But I aways stop what ever I'm doing to write you. I saw your video tape when I was over grandma's house. Grandma and grandady are doing good too. So every thing is "OK".

d.
  r
    o
      p

I heard that Miren is in the drinking program. I haren't seen him in a long time. I saw Mireal just two weeks ago And his kids, Glen mim.. Sorry for the bracking news but Frende dead. About three months ago. I wish I had some more y to give you. But I don't. "People are broke these days". But when I get some I will send you some. When we move to Chciago I will see you a lot when I can. In Novmeber. And I will see the rest of my family. Deon do our family comby to visit you? But to make a long story Short. I'll see you Soon. And I'll keep writing you write me to sometimes. I'll see later.

I'm missing you...   Love all ways.
        And still love you...

Your nafew: Robert "AKA" WooWoo

Chapter 15

Part IX: The Last Dance
Robert

While fate and destiny find their ways through ideological debates, I for one, believe that life has already been written for each of us by an omniscient author; God only knows. "When the Corona virus of 2020 hit, I started to seeing less..." and less of Robert. Whenever he and "Yattie" got together they would call me and give me a hard time about not getting my hair cut and "how long it must be by now!" Robert demonstrated a proclivity to stay busy and the limitations imposed by the virus made no exception he kept accomplishing things. I was so very proud of the man he had become and the veracity of which he approached life and any obstacles put in his way. While I did not approve of everyone in his life, he was his own man and I trusted he would not make the same decisions as those around him did or would.

On a fresh late spring day, my sister, Robert's mother, and I made our way to go see him. They had not seen one another in awhile and it had been too long for me as well. Plus, my hair had grown to...let's just say, I needed a hair cut. We laughed and joked all afternoon as we listened to his mother's fantastical ideas on how to earn a living. At one point Robert interjected with, "let me take a pic of you, to remember you how you was". We didn't know it would be the last picture he we take of us we thought it was one of many more to come. A week later I went back to see Robert and get "lined up" again. One of his regulars was also there and they were talking about going to get Robert a new set of wheels. I still remember the excitement and anxiousness in his voice. He called me later that day to tell me all about the new Audi and I couldn't help but caution him on driving it without a valid drivers license. He replied kindly with, "Oh Unc, you always worrying about the wrong things". I wanted to say more but I let it go and said, "goodbye". "I would have to say it again one last time...", for Robert passed away a few weeks later on May 22, 2020, the day a part of me died too. The things left unsaid were drowned in the regrets of not having done this or that and haunted me as my lil' nephew was gone and I couldn't get him back. I wanted him to be written back into my life by the ultimate author, but as my prayers were many, I knew he was in a better place. He was looking down on me, taking pictures of my life and making sure that they were in the color they needed to be full of life and a fondness of a man that would be missed, my lil' nephew, Robert, may he rest in peace.

We had a memorial for Robert in August of 2020 when we celebrated my father's birthday. We mourned the day of loss of Robert as we celebrated the day of birth for my father a dichotomy of human nature. We also held a special event at a kid's toy store for his surviving children. we sat and observed the legacy that would be his, beautiful children and the moments shared with each of us that held a special place in our hearts moments that would be forever engrained in us. They would serve as a reminder of the frailty of life and how it should be embraced, something Robert did.

CHAPTER 16

MYRAIL

Myrail had stopped by our house on his way to work. He was in a hurry but took the time to jump out shake my hand, meet a guy from my work "Moe" who was there to buy a car from our dad and to give dad a hug. He was there and then he wasn't.

I called Rail on September 5, 2020 to confirm that we were going to get together that weekend in the city. I called him again at 5:30, a time I typically called my wife, but something in his voice earlier was unsettling to me, so I called him instead. He seemed preoccupied and claimed it was caused by being stuck at a kid's party and that he would be leaving soon to head for the city. I ended the call with "See you later big Brother". Anxious to see him, I called again at 8:30 and he told me he was with his family at

Portillios eating delicious hot dogs, I could hear it in his voice. I had a chance to talk with his wife and his son (Glen), I suspect so he could enjoy the rest of his dogs. I hung up the phone with a smile on my face and a warmth in my heart.

I called him again around 11:50 when I was on the road heading towards the city and we discussed having breakfast together in the morning. I hung up with a smile on my face a warmth in my heart.

I would not see Myrail that next morning. That next day would be his last "something happened along the way, and yesterday was all we had", sings Earth Wind and Fire as if they know of loss. If only I could have yesterday back and say all those things I wanted to say; "I love you big bro" just one more time and hang up with a smile and a warmth in my heart one that would last forever.

CHAPTER 17

Part X :Forevers
My Big Brother Myrail

Certain days stick so vividly in our minds its as if they happened only yesterday. I have many fond memories that when I reflect upon my life, they cause me to smile. I have been blessed. September 6, 2020 would forever change my perspective, forever change my life. My brother Myrail has long suffered from chronic asthma, a condition that would attack him, but he would always recover he was my brother, he was a fighter. His wife, Leta, called me in a panic frantically explaining that he was not breathing. She had called the paramedics, so as I dressed to meet them at the hospital, I was confident that this was simply another bout he would win as he had so many times before. I made my way to the hospital in a daze, letting thoughts float aimlessly through my mind never really settling on any one in particular. The parking lot seemed more empty than full and things seemed at ease despite it being a hospital. People I passed greeted me with a smile and I reciprocated. I made it to the fourth floor and I heard the elevator "ding" as the door opened, it was as if a switch went off in the universe everything moved in slow motion, all I could hear was my own breathing and the beating of my very own heart. I took a left and headed towards the nurses station only to be intercepted by Leta. I began to speak but no words came out, for in her eyes she was shouting at me, drowning any sounds coming from me. "What?" I asked repeatedly, "what do you mean?" I then pleaded. "He's gone Scotchie...your brother...he's gone," the voice answered back like a narrator in a movie, in a dream or nightmare or whatever it was to be called.

My whole entire world folded in on itself with me in the center. "I just talked to him yesterday," ran through my mind over and over again in attempts to prove the news false "it just can't be!" Death was not new to me, the environment I grew up in leant itself to such tragedy but when it is your blood, your brother, another part of you you die too. There are no words for the pain; because it is not there. When you mistakenly hit your finger with a hammer there is a physical pain that is unmistaken you feel it. In Rail's passing I was instead filled with...a nothingness so deep that it hurt from the inside out. There is a desperation in such emptiness, but nothing to fill it it is a desolate place with no cure or words to express it or fix it. So....I wept.

People came from all around to pay their respects, people I had not seen in years and under any other circumstance it would have been a joy to have seen them. There were coworkers from Whirlpool and family from Chicago, Leta's and our family from Ohio, Ricky and Yvonne came from Milwaukee and even my Aunt Rhoda came from Atlanta. It is interesting how people express their sadness so differently; some laugh a lot to mask the pain, whereas others become very quiet and withdrawn and others let out their anguish in tears. Tacora and Boosie, hosted the gathering following the funeral procession. There was a large oversized picture of Myrail in the hallway, it shot right through you as his infectious smile pierced your heart and there was no protection from it.

I pictured me as calm and stoic, a pillar, when I went to his casket or reminisced with others, but in reality that would prove not to be the case...I wept like no other man I have seen. The tears that mixed with the pain burned, but I couldn't stop it. "He's never coming back, my big brother is never coming home," I cried into my father's shoulder as he tried his best to comfort me through his own pain and overwhelming sense of loss.

In my head I hear his voice and in my heart I feel him. The pain from the emptiness may never be filled again, but as I grow older, the memories of him stay strong in me. I hold onto those times that he was there for me, when he protected me, when he lead me like big brothers do. It was a warm fall day that had an autumn sun so bright that you knew he was present, he was among us. I could feel it with all that I am my big brother was there...and...he was smiling. I do not think the hole left in me will be completely filled, but I know that I am blessed to have had him in my life and I am the better for it and in that I find some solace. What I wouldn't give for just another day with him. And in time I will be with him again, but for now I live in a manner to honor him and those that have gone before me. I love my big brother and I always will~

CHAPTER 18

Robert

"You would think that the more..." we are exposed to something the more accustomed to it we become. You would expect to build a tolerance or develop an immunity. When it comes to death and dying however, there is no vaccine, there is no threshold of protection it always hurts, especially when it is one you love. You never get used to it, nor do I want to. I would rather feel the pain that reminds me that I loved and was loved, than to be numb to the experience that is life. If we could only turn back time and undo that which we have done to put things back in their place as they once were. If only. Rather, we are faced with dealing with the reality as it is before us; the pain, the sorrow, the anguish and all that is a part of losing someone we love.

It had been too many days since I had talked to Robert so I gave him a call. There was no answer. A few hours later I tried again. There was no answer. Once, I can accept, but twice? That was not like Robert no matter what the circumstances. I decided to call my mother and inquired if she had spoken to Robert recently and she told me that she had not and offered that; "it is possible that he is just out of town." I accepted the possibility for a moment but soon denied such an explanation for if he was out of town he was more likely to pick up; "Hey Unc, I'm outta town, gotta run I'll catch you later and don't tell grandma." Her efforts certainly did not placate my growing concern. By the third day I had had enough and I convinced mom to go with me to see Robert when we both got off of work. When I saw my mothers face I wanted to tell her what I was feeling I was worried that something was wrong and moms have a way of putting things right. Instead I refrained. When I saw Robert's car "...in the parking lot, any suspicion I had, manifested into a..." reality in my mind something was definitely wrong. I didn't want to face anything remotely close to what my mind had conjured up in my imagination. It is amazing what the mind is capable of at times.

I watched as my mother methodically slid her spare key into the key hole, I heard the locking mechanism "click". I was entirely aware of my senses and I wasn't breathing. She slowly pushed open the door and before she had it all the way open I saw him lying on the floor face down. "Oh, he's only sleeping," my mother offered. I knew better. "Stop mom," I instructed as I placed both of my hands gently on her shoulders. "We need to get outta here," I commanded, "there might be someone still in here." "I could feel her body shaking..." as I guided her out of the room with my hand on the small of her back. I closed the door behind me and I could feel my own hand shaking as it made contact with the door knob. To say we were hysterical would be a misdescription for at that moment we were inundated with an awe that seemed to freeze us in the moment. She called the police as I tried to find my breath and as we waited our emotions began to thaw allowing a hysteria to set in. First my mother, and then I would follow when we were escorted down to the police station for questioning. We were the ones who found him so we were the ones being questioned.

The authorities asked me a series of questions, one of which to this day I do not recall. I could not speak at times as I was overwhelmed with a remorse that drowned me I could hardly breath through the choking tears as I fought to respond to their inquiries. "Robert, my lil' nephew is gone," I kept saying to myself similar to the words I replayed in my mind not too many months part about to follow about Myrail. The injustice of it, the unfairness of it for them, for me how could life be so cruel and so cold?

His passing drove a wedge in the family at a time "...when one would expect it would bring..."us together. With no closure, accepting the event can haunt you, can cause a wall to be erected and those walls served to close us out from one another this only manifested into regrets of various dynamics and a vindictiveness that had no target. So, we directed it at each other at the ones we loved, the easiest of targets.

They held a candlelight vigil at Robert's complex and many were in attendance according to the superintendent when we went to gather his personal belongings. The flames of the candles have since burned out, but I wear a bullet chain with Robert's ashes as a light for my own path one to honor his memory. My beloved Robert, the lil' nephew that taught me so much in the living of life that I will miss him with each breath and for the rest of my tomorrows.

CHAPTER 19

Part XI: Back Down Memory Lane
Myrail

Can you ever right or speak highly enough of a departed loved one? I believe that there are core things that need be expressed, and anything beyond that is the color that creates a brighter image. "Colorful" is certainly an adjective to describe Myrail. I worked for him at Whirlpool, and despite the fact he was a mess, he made sure his department worked hard. As soon as I would pull out my phone to make a call, he would appear out of nowhere (just like he did that day to help from the burn of the hot grease); "hey, that's on your time not on my time". I would often stand and watch other guys fixing things and sure enough he would drive by in his little cart as if magically appearing through some worm hole; "you got your hands folded like you workin' Minister Louis Farrakhan

Security". There was never a dull moment with him. When I first started at Whirlpool, I would bum a ride with Yattie, but eventually rode with Myrail. He would pick me up for the fortyminute trip and we would always stop at the same gas station and he would get his soda in a Styrofoam cup along with some hot dogs, cigs and sometimes even gas. He would crank the music bringing to life the stillness of the night that led to the third shift the graveyard.

Oh how far we had come since those days of flippen' burgers and dunkin' fries at Burger King. Yes, we were adults, but certain things stayed with us from our childhood and cereal was one of them. Often times we didn't have much, but there was always cereal. "So, after our shift we would often indulge in a big bowl ..." of cereal. Two big "kids" eatin' their Lucky Charms and loving every minute of it. I don't know if it was"... the fact we both served time, but we appreciated the opportunity..."and to make something of ourselves despite the odd hours. We made the most with what we had. "... We would always communicate. Even after I moved on to lead another team ,he would come by ..."my department to see how I was doing. We would talk most nights after work, sometimes just about small things and other times on the larger things.

Today, many of those"... words shared are forgotten ,but the message ..."in them remains and shall forever. We were brothers. There is a saying that infers that friends are more special than family because we choose our friends and not our family. For me I was blessed, as while Myrail was my biological brother he was my best friend a choice we both "...made of one another naturally, just as we..." was the love we shared for one another. "I will miss him, the time we shared, and all of those..." that we will not Brother Love, Myrail, Brother Love.

CHAPTER 20

Robert

I am always intrigued by" vision boards" and what images people select to express their aspirations. Robert's was no exception, but with his he included a list of those things he had already achieved. I never worked with Robert, but he did have his stint with Myrail at Whirlpool after I left. "Robert would call me after his shift all excited about things and I could ..."hear the great anticipation in his voice and how he too was subject to Myrail's humor and ridicule just as I had been. I would talk to him about medical insurance or about the importance of maximizing his contributions to his 401(k). Man, how far we had come since running the streets "401(k)'s and cafeteria plans" go figure. Robert was focused on getting his own place just prior to his passing and had made great strides in such regard. I was so very proud of him. Robert was a dreamer one of the biggest dreamers of us all. But, he was also an achiever one of the biggest of us all everything considered.

Whenever he would call me for advice I would keep it straight and when he did not get the answer he was looking for he did not complain. Instead, he kept moving forward determined to reach his destination that place where fate and destiny meet whether either are ready or not. The universe took him from us too early and his presence is missed but his spirit remains he is here in his songs and those actions that moved us. I will watch videos with him in them where he is cutting hair or doing this or that, and in them all there is that smile. The infectious expression that life is enjoyable to him and he is living it on his terms. I am his "big Unc" and he is my "lil' nephew" that had a big impact on me while he lived and an even larger impact now that he is gone all the best lil' nephew and see you on the other side.

Deon Harris

CHAPTER 21

Part XII:Another Part of Me:
Common species & Exceptional **Love**

Incarceration, the loss of liberties and freedoms, forces a new perspective. The global pandemic of recent has exposed millions to a mere modicum of what imprisonment is like. In such state, communicating with your loved ones is critical. I saved every letter that Myrail wrote to me during my incarceration. Doing so served as more than a sentimental gesture, but as a bedrock of my psychological state to combat the ominous loneliness that incarceration brings. Then, in the last week of my captivity, I burned them, "I burned them all", proverbially that is. Ironically, I had to leave behind that same thing that kept me strong during my incarceration that would make me weak following it. I needed to remember the loss of liberty and freedom to maintain perspective of such luxuries, but I did not need to relive the daily pains.

With Robert however, I saved all of the letters for they served to remind me of the intestinal fortitude it takes to overcome certain obstacles, like a 42 year sentence not to mention the divine province that I believe had a hand in our fortunes. To say, "I miss" these men would be an understatement of grand proportion; as I planned on growing old with them. The visions of my future were ripped from me leaving me with only the images of yesterday. So, I pen these words to the world in hopes of extending their lives as long as the pages remain. It is a brief glimpse into the lives of two men, Myrail and Robert, that may remind others of others just like them that they have or had in their lives. Albeit it is brief, but hopefully enough to impress upon others to recognize the greatness in those around us before it is too late. For in "the absence there is a void we often..." do not know how to fill. We break and are not sure how to be fixed. There is no manual or repair guide. I endeavor to keep their memory alive through these pages and in the way I lead my life. My loss is not limited to me, for many have known the loss of a loved one, they have felt the devastating effects of such absence. I have simply chosen to write it down and to share that we are not alone in our pains, struggles and challenges.

Through it all however, there is a peace on the other side that we can find, or it may even find us. It is as if the greater the pain, the greater the peace that enfolds us, giving us purpose and direction. I saw the pain in Myrail when Robert passed, as did others. I also saw the pride that Myrail had in me even though he had a unique way of showing it. Robert smiled every day past, so I smile every day present and future. Two men that I knew as boys to one I was "lil' bro" and to the other "big Unc".

They were as unique as they were alike, so I embrace their similarities and their differences.

I loved them both and yes we had our ups and downs just as they did between them as well. But that's what family does, that's what friends do, they challenge one another and in the end the relationship is the strongest for it.

We were bound by blood that grew stronger through friendship, a bond that would not be broken even in death. It will live on in the livingin the hearts and minds of those that they left behind; me, us, we.

As a species we share common traits and it is my hopes that reading these pages about these men, men that you may have never met, you will see the magic that was in them by the way they impacted those around them. My "Big Bro " Myrail and" lil" Nephew "Robert lived lives of great moments and they will forever be remembered may they Rest In Peace with there Heavenly Father knowing a calmness and contentment that they deserve. Brother Love

ABOUT THE AUTHOR

Deon Harris is an up and coming author that has already published part one of the major novel series, "Dog Food" and two novellas, "The Basic Essentials of Doing Time Constructively: Prison Politics" and "The Door Swings Both Ways". He now brings his fourth literary effort in "Memories in an Iowa Glass".

Mr. Harris is committed to giving back to his community in his motivational speaking and on going literary contributions that delve into the spirit and soul of our culture. He has maintained an incredibly positive attitude and outlook on life despite his trials and tribulations. His losses have made him more of a man than his successes and he is always willing to share his journey with others. He is a prolific story teller that hopes this piece of him in literature, "Memories in an Iowa Glass", is relatable and will inspire his readers to continue to embrace the "blessed" life that is around them... others.

Order Form
Make **Money Orders** PayableTo:

Deon Harris – 319-450-5423

QTY	Available Publications	Price

Ship To:

Name: _____

Address: _____

City: _____ State: _____ Zip: _____

For Shipping and Handling: Add $3.75 for 1st Book. Add $1.75 for each additional book. All books are also available on Amazon and Kindle. All titles coming soon, also can be preordered.

We Help You Self-Publish Your Book

You're The Publisher and We're Your Legs!
We Offer Editing For An Extra Fee, and Highly
Suggest It, If Waved, We Print What You Submit!

Crystell Publications is not your publisher, but we will help you selfpublish your own novel.

Ask About our Payment Plans

Crystal Perkins, MHR
Essence Magazine Bestseller
PO BOX 8044 / Edmond – OK 73083
www.crystellpublications.com
(405) 4143991

Plan 1A 190 250 pgs. $699.00   Plan 1B 150 180 pgs. $674.00
Plan 1C 70   145pgs $625.00

2 (Publisher/Printer) Proofs, Correspondence, 3 books, Manuscript Scan and Conversion, Typeset, Masters, Custom Cover, ISBN, Promo in Mink, 2 issues of Mink Magazine, Consultation, POD uploads. 1 Week of Eblast to a reading population of over 5000 readers, book clubs, and bookstores, The Authors Guide to Understanding The POD, and writing Tips, and a review snippet along with a professional query letter will be sent to our top 4 distributors in an attempt to have your book shelved in their bookstores or distributed to potential book vendors. After the query is sent, if interested in your book, distributors will contact you or your outside rep to discuss shipment of books, and fees.

Plan 2A 190 250 pgs. $645.00   Plan 2B 150 180 pgs.
$600.00
Plan 2C 70   145pgs $550.00

1 Printer Proof, Correspondence, 3 books, Manuscript Scan and Conversion, Typeset, Masters, Custom Cover, ISBN, Promo in Mink, 1 issue of Mink Magazine, Consultation, POD upload.

Made in the USA
Columbia, SC
07 September 2021

44474870R00075